JAMIE CULLUM
THE PURSUIT

© 2009 by International Music Publications Ltd
First published by International Music Publications Ltd in 2009
International Music Publications Ltd is a Faber Music company
Bloomsbury House 74–77 Great Russell Street
London WC1B 3DA

Arranged by Paul Honey & Olly Weeks
Edited by Lucy Holliday & Alex Davis

Photography: Kit Lynch-Robinson
Technical Photographer: Anthony Dickenson
Director of Photography: Dan Bronks
Additional Photography: Marc Silver
Art Direction: Sacha Lynch-Robinson, www.spencertrace.co.uk
Creative Director: Marc Silver, www.marcsilver.net
Faber Music Artwork: Lydia Merrills-Ashcroft

Printed in England by Caligraving Ltd

The text paper used in this publication is a virgin fibre product
that is manufactured in the UK to ISO 14001 standards. The
wood fibre used is only sourced from managed forests using
sustainable forestry principles. This paper is 100% recyclable

ISBN10: 0-571-53397-3
EAN13: 978-0-571-53397-8

To buy Faber Music publications or to find out about the full
range of titles available, please contact your local music retailer
or Faber Music sales enquiries:

Faber Music Ltd, Burnt Mill, Elizabeth Way, Harlow,
CM20 2HX England
Tel: +44(0)1279 82 89 82
Fax: +44(0)1279 82 89 83
sales@fabermusic.com fabermusic.com

05 **JUST ONE OF THOSE THINGS**

16 **I'M ALL OVER IT**

22 **WHEELS**

28 **IF I RULED THE WORLD**

33 **YOU AND ME ARE GONE**

43 **DON'T STOP THE MUSIC**

50 **LOVE AIN'T GONNA LET YOU DOWN**

55 **MIXTAPE**

62 **I THINK, I LOVE**

66 **WE RUN THINGS**

72 **NOT WHILE I'M AROUND**

77 **MUSIC IS THROUGH**

87 **I GET ALONG WITHOUT YOU VERY WELL**

92 **EVERYONE'S LONELY**

100 **GRACE IS GONE**

103 **GRAN TORINO**

JUST ONE OF THOSE THINGS

Words and Music by Cole Porter

here's_____ hop-ing we'll meet____ now and then.____ It was

great fun,____ but it was just one of those

things._____ One of those

___ things._____

I'M ALL OVER IT

Words and Music by Jamie Cullum and Ricky Ross

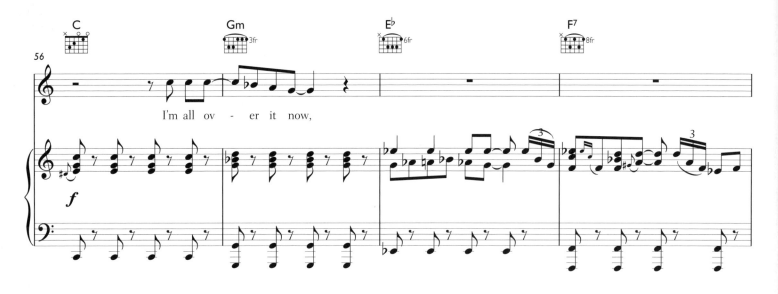

I'm all ov - er it now,

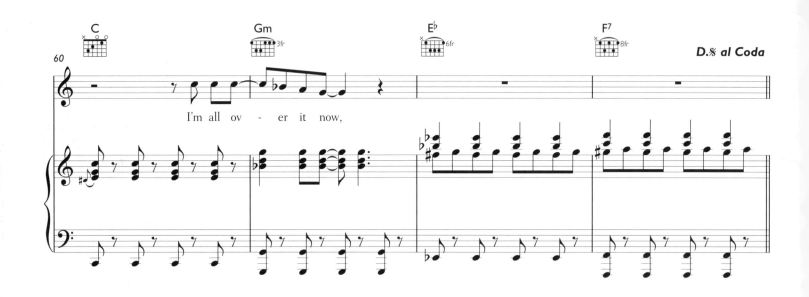

D.𝄋 al Coda

I'm all ov - er it now,

⊕ Coda

freely

Yeah.

mp

Ped.

WHEELS

Words and Music by Jamie Cullum and Ben Cullum

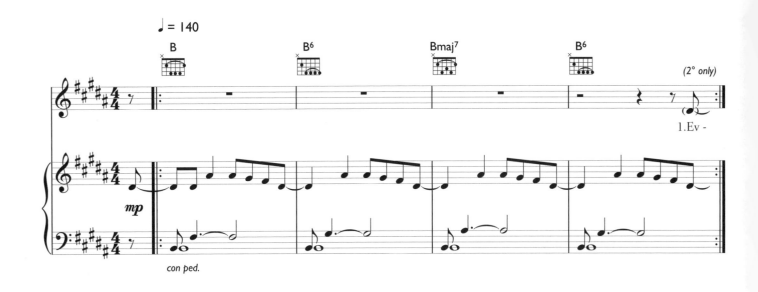

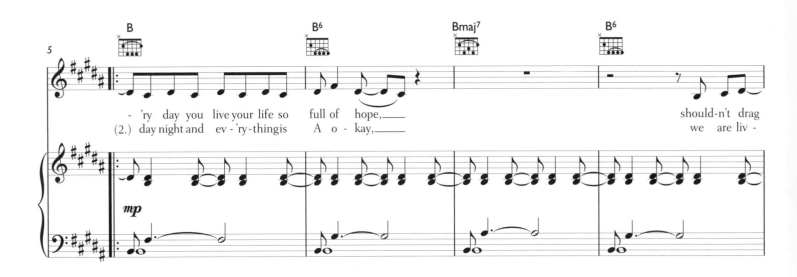

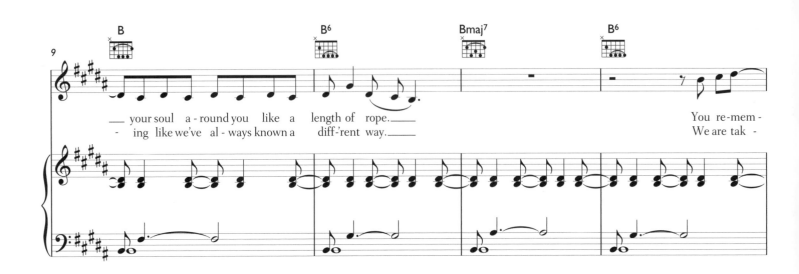

IF I RULED THE WORLD

Words by Leslie Bricusse
Music by Cyril Ornadel

man   in the moon has   when the moon - beams._____

YOU AND ME ARE GONE

Words and Music by Jamie Cullum, Geoff Gascoyne and Sebastiaan de Krom

1. Ev - 'ry time___ I see___ what's writ - ten on___ your mind___
2. Truth - ful - ly___ I've got a mo - dus o - pe - ran - di,

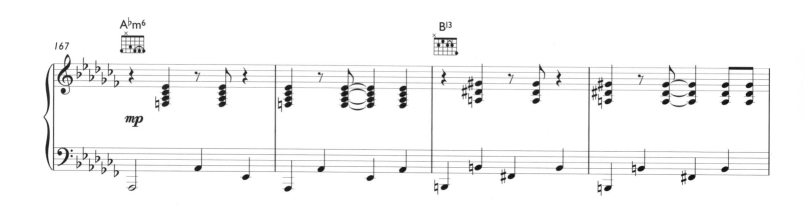

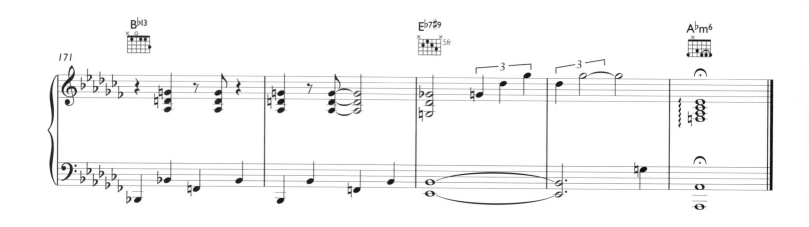

DON'T STOP THE MUSIC

Words and Music by Michael Jackson, Mikkel Eriksen,
Tor Erik Hermansen and Frankie Storm

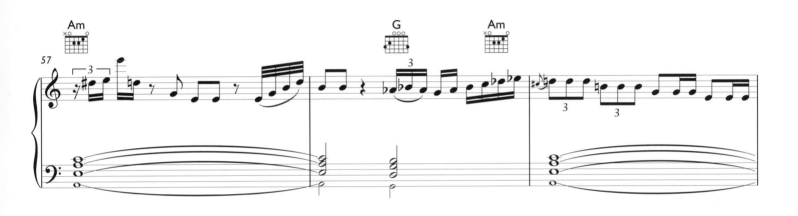

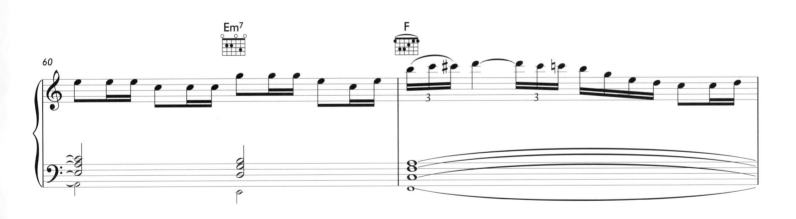

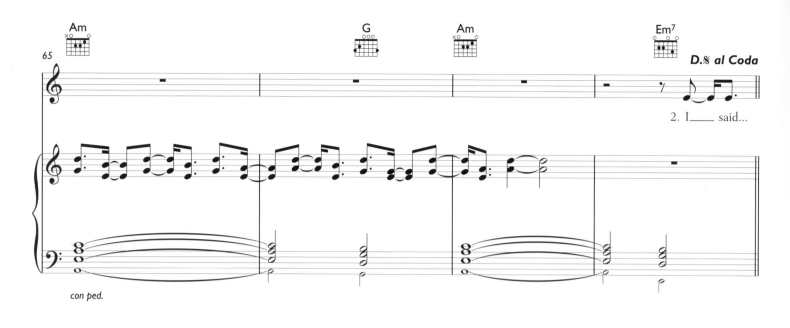

2. I____ said...

Coda

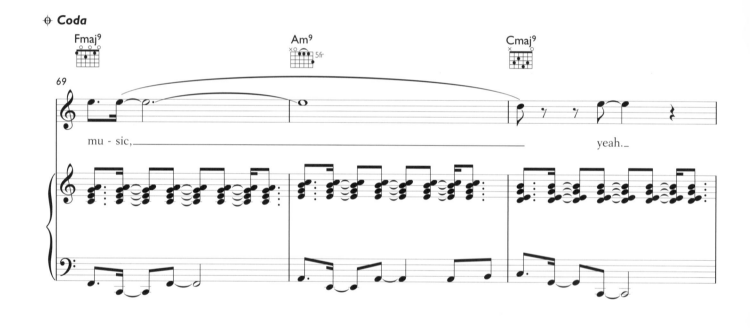

mu - sic,_____ yeah.__

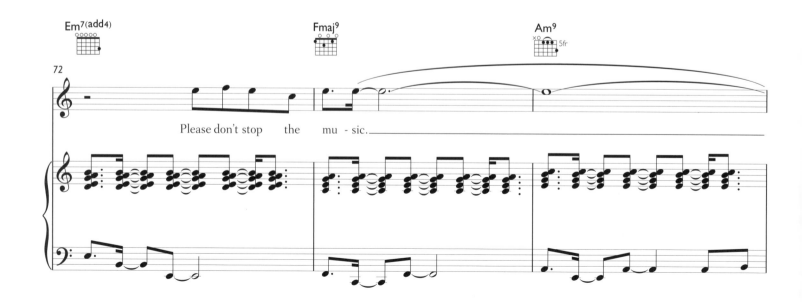

Please don't stop the mu - sic._____

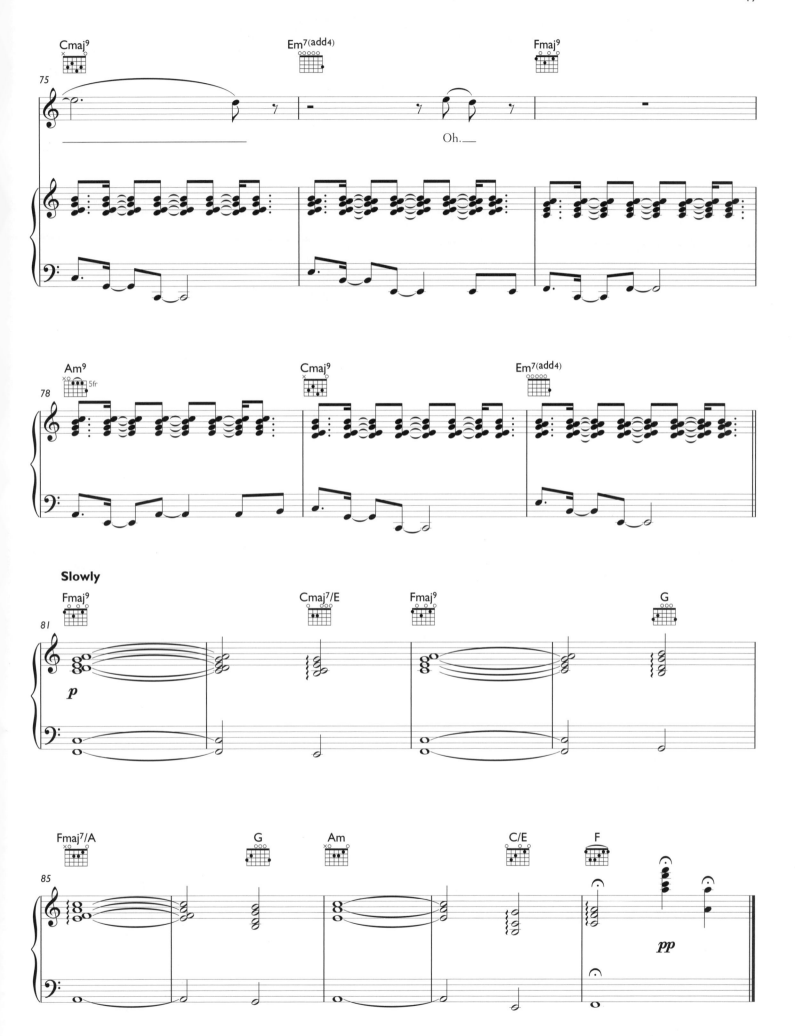

LOVE AIN'T GONNA LET YOU DOWN

Words and Music by Jamie Cullum

Feel it burn-ing like a Bom-bay gin, a thou-sand sum-mers graz-ing on your skin, rest-less-ly an-ti-ci-pat-ing so ma-ny ti - ny things. The pur-suit of love con-sumes us all, I'll be your Fab-rice with-out the war, do you dream a-bout it writ-ten for, burst - ing with all___ the weight

MIXTAPE

Words and Music by Jamie Cullum and Ben Cullum

I THINK, I LOVE

Words and Music by Jamie Cullum

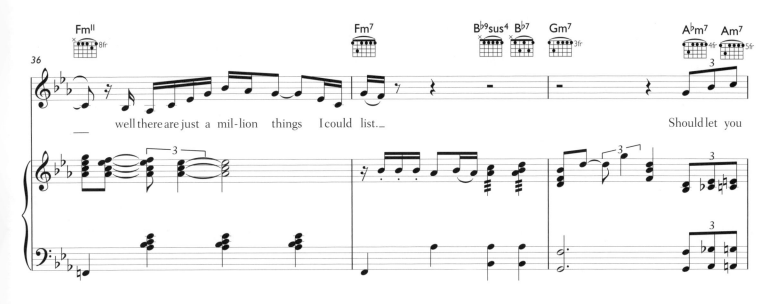

well there are just a mil-lion things I could list._ Should let you

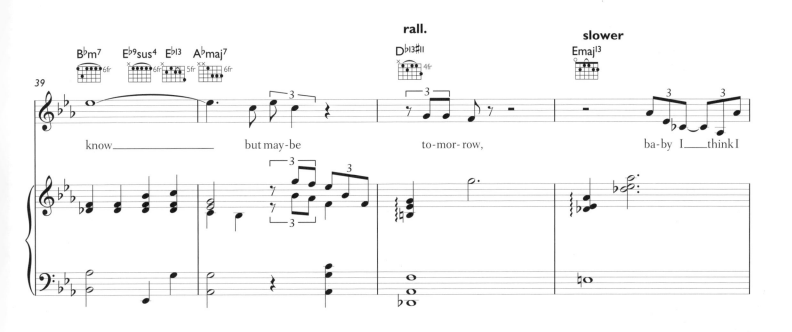

rall. **slower**

know_____ but may-be to-mor-row, ba-by I___think I

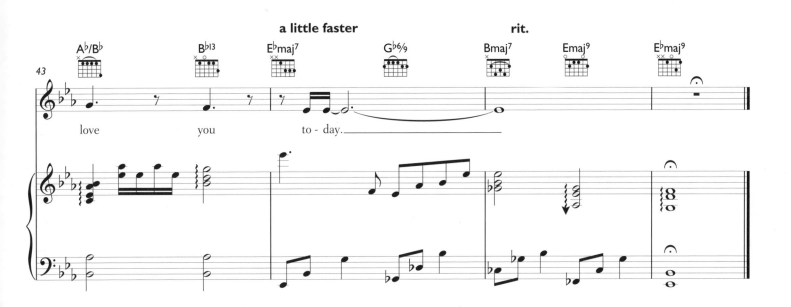

a little faster **rit.**

love you to - day._____

WE RUN THINGS

Words and Music by Jamie Cullum, Ben Cullum and Karl Gordon

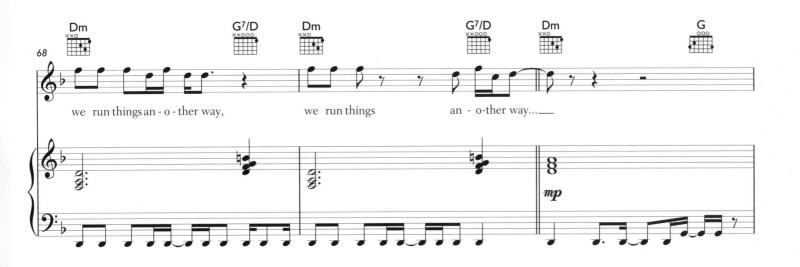

we run things an - o - ther way,   we run things   an - o - ther way...

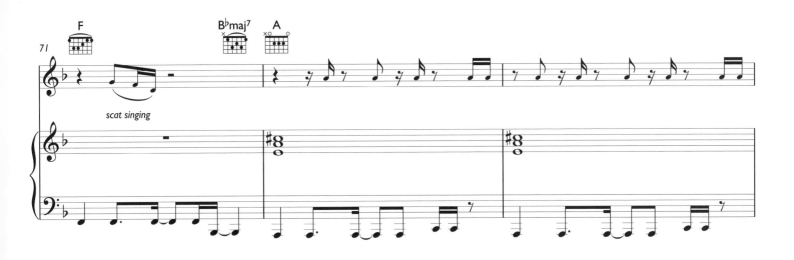

scat singing

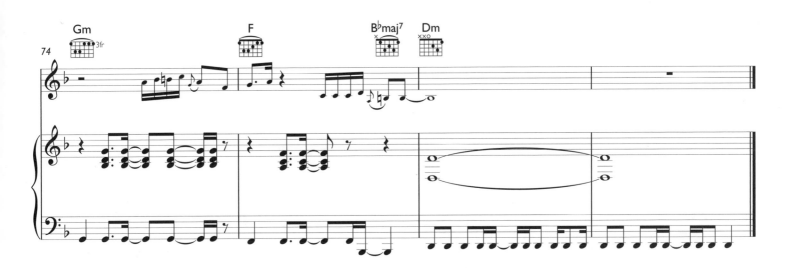

NOT WHILE I'M AROUND

(FROM "SWEENEY TODD")

Words and Music by Stephen Sondheim

MUSIC IS THROUGH

Words and Music by Jamie Cullum and Ben Cullum

1.If_____ you wan - na get with me,_____ then you've got - ta

2.If_____ you wan - na fuck with me,_____ lord you'll nev - er

Girl I got your num - ber, call you when the mu - sic is through.

I GET ALONG WITHOUT YOU VERY WELL

Words by Hoagy Carmichael and George Terry
Music by Hoagy Carmichael

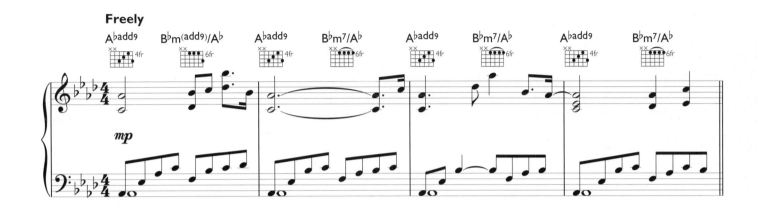

1. I get a-long with-out you ve-ry well, of course I do, ex-cept when
2. I've for-got-ten you just like I should, of course I have, ex-cept to

soft rains fall, a drip from leaves then I___ re-call the thrill of be-ing shel-tered in your
hear your name, or some-one's laugh that is___ the same. 'Cos I've for-got-en you just like I

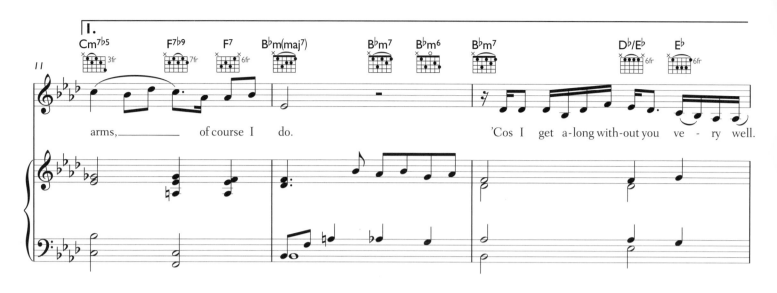

arms,_____ of course I do.

'Cos I get a-long with-out you ve - ry well.

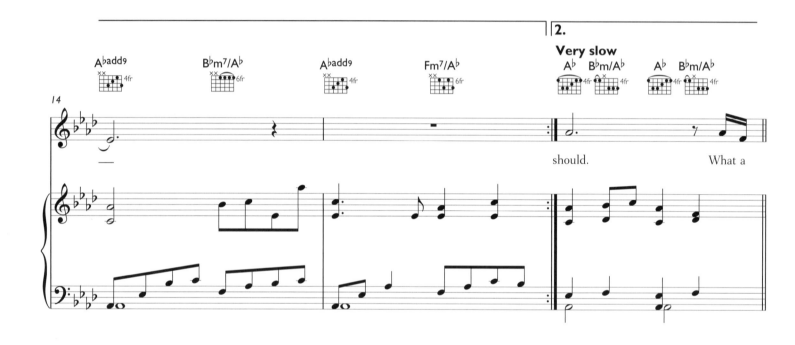

_____ should.

What a

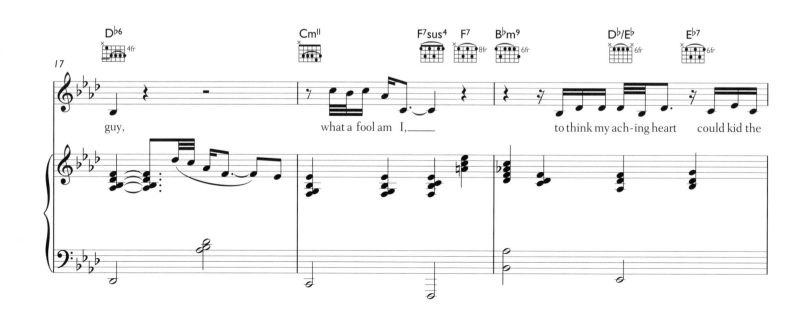

guy,

what a fool am I,_____

to think my ach-ing heart could kid the

EVERYONE'S LONELY

Words and Music by Jamie Cullum and Ben Cullum

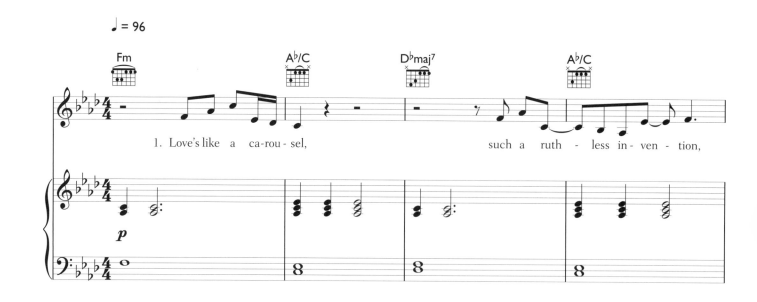

1. Love's like a ca-rou - sel, such a ruth - less in - ven - tion,

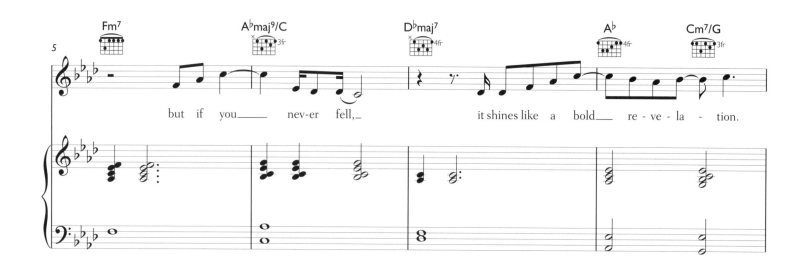

but if you___ nev-er fell,___ it shines like a bold___ re-ve-la - tion.

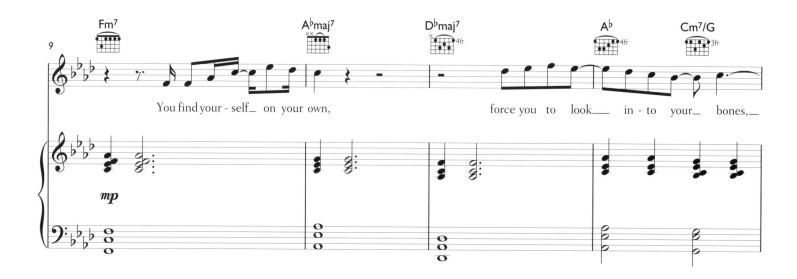

You find your-self___ on your own, force you to look___ in-to your___ bones,___

- ly these days, did I men-tion that_ you should__ stay?_____

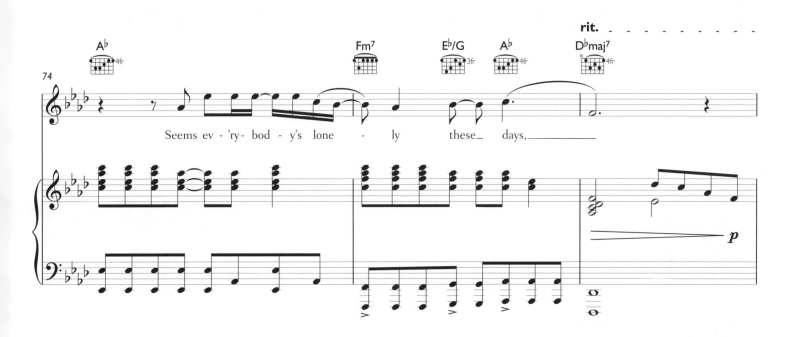

Seems ev - 'ry- bod - y's lone - ly these_ days,_____

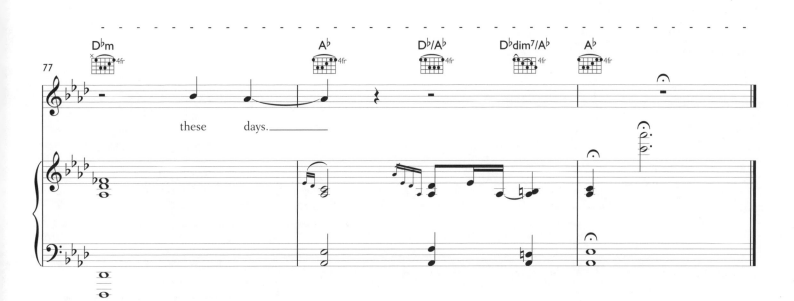

these days._____

GRACE IS GONE

Words and Music by Clint Eastwood and Carole Bayer Sager

Original key Db major

♩ = 72

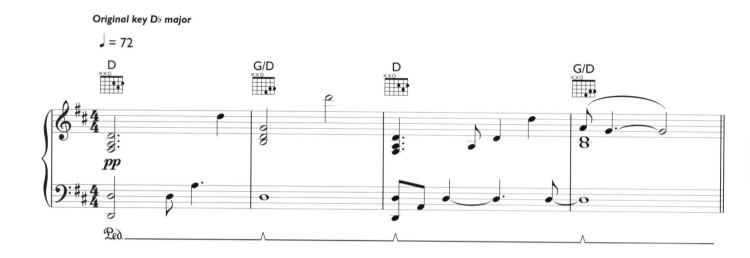

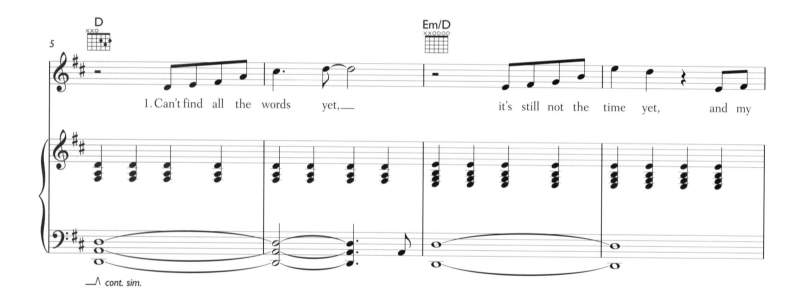

1. Can't find all the words yet,___ it's still not the time yet, and my mind can't think of an-y-thing, it on-ly sees___ you.___ 2. You know I am

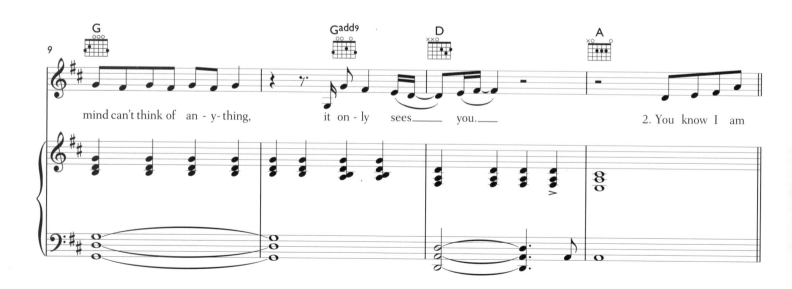

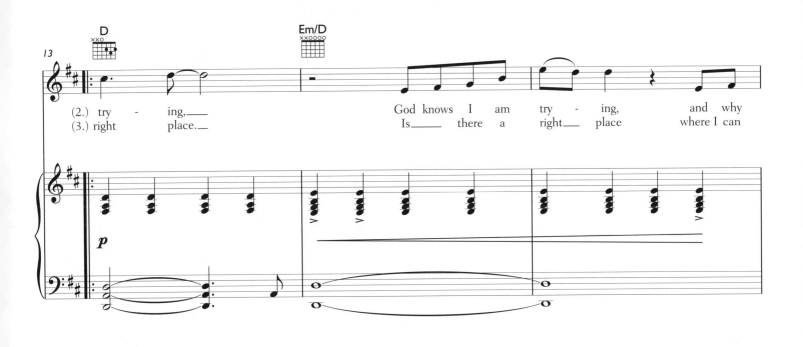

GRAN TORINO

Words and Music by Kyle C Eastwood, Michael C Stevens,
Clint Eastwood and Jamie Cullum

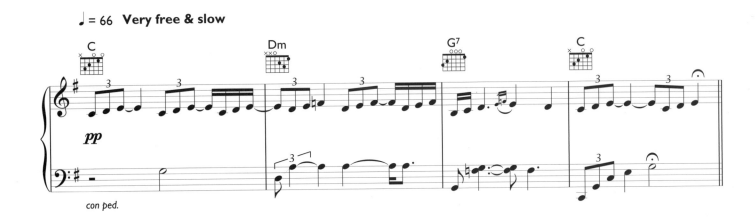

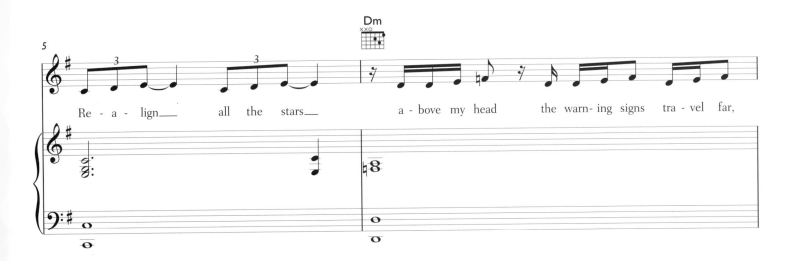

Re - a - lign___ all the stars___ a - bove my head the warn - ing signs tra - vel far,

I drink in - stead___ on my own, oh, how I've known the bat - tle scars and worn out beds.